Ready·Set·Learn.....

Beginning Math

Pre·K Through K

180+ Stickers Inside

Managing Editor	***Teacher Created Resources, Inc.***
Ina Massler Levin, M.A.	6421 Industry Way
	Westminster, CA 92683
Editor	www.teachercreated.com
Eric Migliaccio	**ISBN: 978-1-4206-5953-5**
Contributing Editor	*©2007 Teacher Created Resources, Inc.*
Sarah Smith	Reprinted, 2010 (PO4197)
Creative Director	Made in U.S.A.
Karen J. Goldfluss, M.S. Ed.	

Cover Design

Tony Carrillo / Marilyn Goldberg

Teacher Created Resources

This book belongs to

_____

Ready·Set·Learn

Get Ready to Learn!

Get ready, get set, and go! Boost your child's learning with this exciting series of books. Geared to help children practice and master many needed skills, the *Ready·Set·Learn* books are bursting with 64 pages of learning fun. Use these books for . . .

☀ enrichment   ☀ skills reinforcement   ☀ extra practice

With their smaller size, the *Ready·Set·Learn* books fit easily in children's hands, backpacks, and book bags. All your child needs to get started are pencils, crayons, and colored pencils.

A full sheet of colorful stickers is included. Use these stickers for . . .

☀ decorating pages

☀ rewarding outstanding effort

☀ keeping track of completed pages

Celebrate your child's progress by using these stickers on the reward chart located on the inside cover. The blue-ribbon sticker fits perfectly on the certificate on page 64.

With *Ready·Set·Learn* and a little encouragement, your child will be on the fast track to learning fun!

Biggest

Directions: Color the biggest object in each row.

1.

2.

3.

4.

 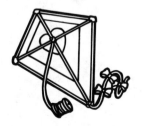

Smallest

Directions: Color the smallest object in each row.

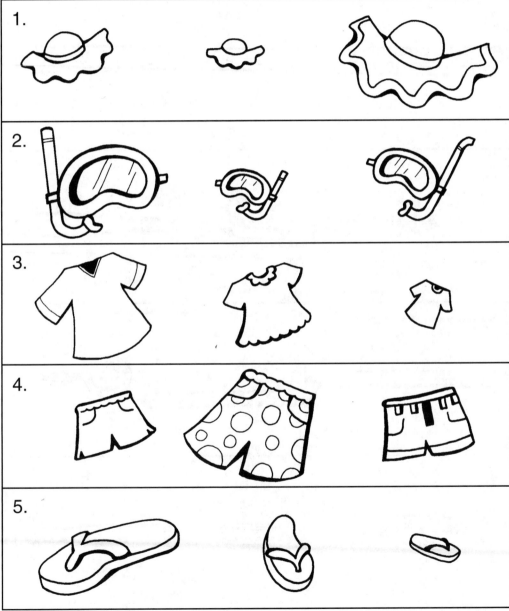

Longest

Directions: Color the longest object in each row.

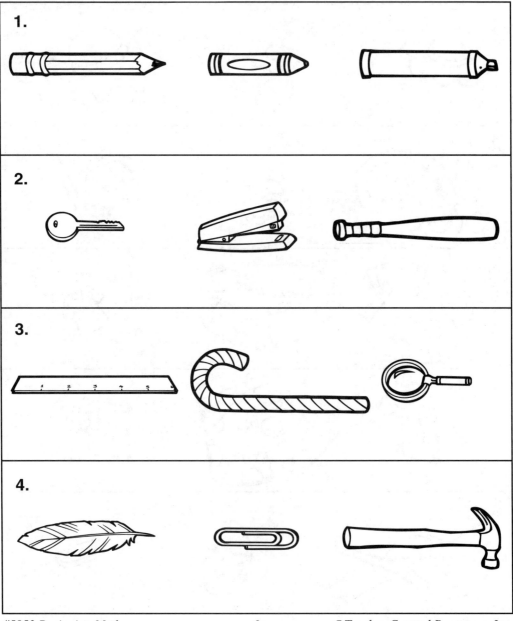

Shortest

Directions: Color the shortest object in each row.

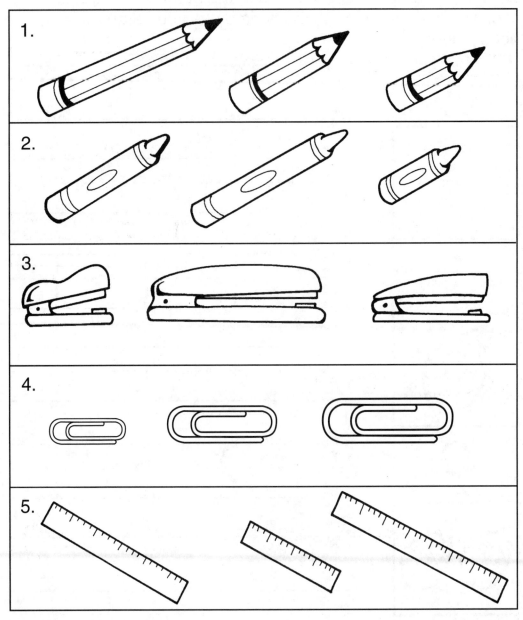

Zero, One, and Two

Directions: Look at the number on top of each box. That's how many are in the picture. Trace the numbers on the top line. Write the number as many times as you can on the bottom line.

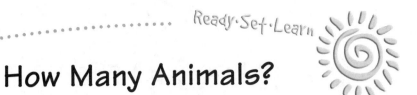

How Many Animals?

Directions: Look at the number in each row. Which picture shows that many animals? Circle the picture with that many animals. Draw a big **X** over the picture that does not show that many animals.

0		
1		
2		

Three and Four

Directions: Look at the number on top of each box. That's how many are in the picture. Trace the numbers on the top line. Write the number as many times as you can on the bottom lines.

3

4

How Many Animals?

Directions: Look at the number in each row. Which picture shows that many animals? Circle the picture with that many animals. Draw a big **X** over the picture that does not show that many animals.

3		
4		
4		
3		

Five and Six

Directions: Look at the number on top of each box. That's how many are in the picture. Trace the numbers on the top line. Write the number as many times as you can on the bottom lines.

5

5 5 5 5

5

6

6 6 6 6

6

12

How Many Animals?

Directions: Look at the number in each row. Which picture shows that many animals? Circle the picture with that many animals. Draw a big **X** over the picture that does not show that many animals.

5		
6		
5		
6		

Seven and Eight

Directions: Look at the number on top of each box. That's how many are in the picture. Trace the numbers on the top line. Write the number as many times as you can on the bottom lines.

7

7 7 7 7

7

8

8 8 8 8

8

How Many Animals?

Directions: Look at the number in each row. Which picture shows that many animals? Circle the picture with that many animals. Draw a big **X** over the picture that does not show that many animals.

Nine and Ten

Directions: Look at the number on the top of each box. That's how many are in the picture. Trace the numbers on the top line. Write the number as many times as you can on the bottom lines.

9

9 9 9 9

9

10

10 10 10

10

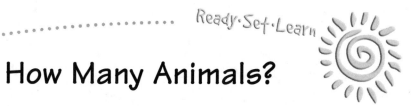

How Many Animals?

Directions: Look at the number in each row. Which picture shows that many animals? Circle the picture with that many animals. Draw a big **X** over the picture that does not show that many animals.

9		
10		
9		
10		

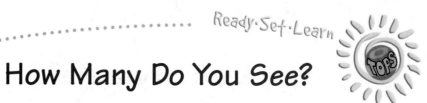

How Many Do You See?

Directions: Circle the number of objects in each box. The first one has been done for you.

1 2 ③	1 2 3
1 2 3	1 2 3
1 2 3	1 2 3

Acorns Everywhere!

Directions: Circle the number of acorns in each box. The first one has been done for you.

1 2 3 ④ 5 6 7	1 2 3 4 5 6 7
1 2 3 4 5 6 7	1 2 3 4 5 6 7
1 2 3 4 5 6 7	1 2 3 4 5 6 7

Leaves All Around

Directions: Circle the number of leaves in each box.

1 2 3 4 5 6 7	1 2 3 4 5 6 7
1 2 3 4 5 6 7	1 2 3 4 5 6 7
1 2 3 4 5 6 7	1 2 3 4 5 6 7

Busy Buses

Directions: Circle the number of buses in each box.

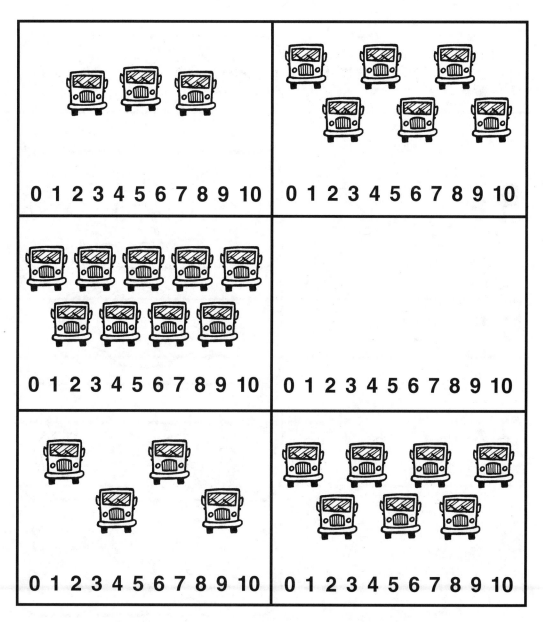

Bunches of Numbers

Directions: Draw a line from the number to the matching set. Begin at the dot.

1 •

3 •

5 •

2 •

4 •

22

Bunches of Numbers

Directions: Draw a line from the number to the matching set.
Begin at the dot.

8•

10•

7•

9•

6•

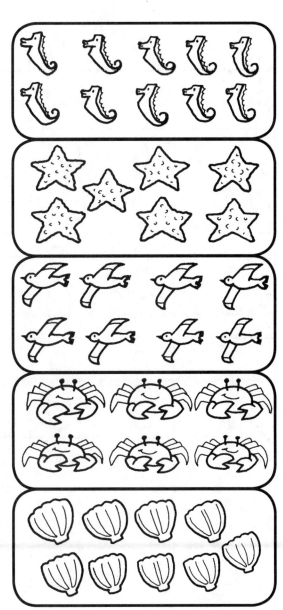

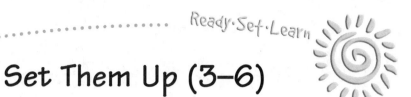

Set Them Up (3–6)

Directions: Write the number of bowling pins in each row. Use the numbers below to help you.

	(4 pins)
	(6 pins)
	(3 pins)
	(5 pins)

3	4	5	6

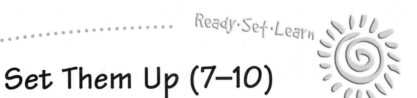

Set Them Up (7–10)

Directions: Write the number of bowling pins in each row. Use the numbers below to help you.

	(10 bowling pins)
	(8 bowling pins)
	(9 bowling pins)
	(7 bowling pins)

7	8	9	10

Butterfly Effect

Directions: Add one more spot to each butterfly and circle the total number of spots that are now on the butterfly.

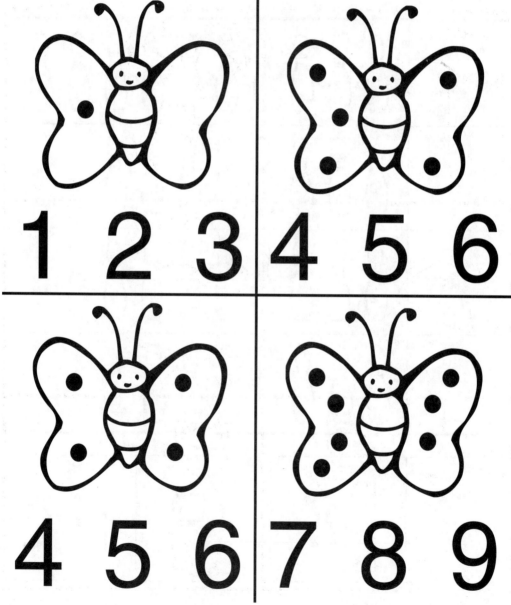

Count the Objects

Directions: On the line, write the number of objects that are in each box.

Bouncing Balls

Directions: Write the number of balls in each box on the line.

Weather Objects

Directions: Write the number of objects that are in each box on the line.

_____

_____

_____

_____

_____

_____

Count the Smiles

Directions: Draw the number of smiling faces in each box on the line.

Hearts and Flowers

Directions: Count the objects. Write the number on the line.

Where's He Hiding?

Directions: Connect the dots from 1–10 to see where the magician has hidden the rabbit. Color your picture.

Up, Up, and Away

Directions: Some of the numbers on the balloons are missing! Write them in.

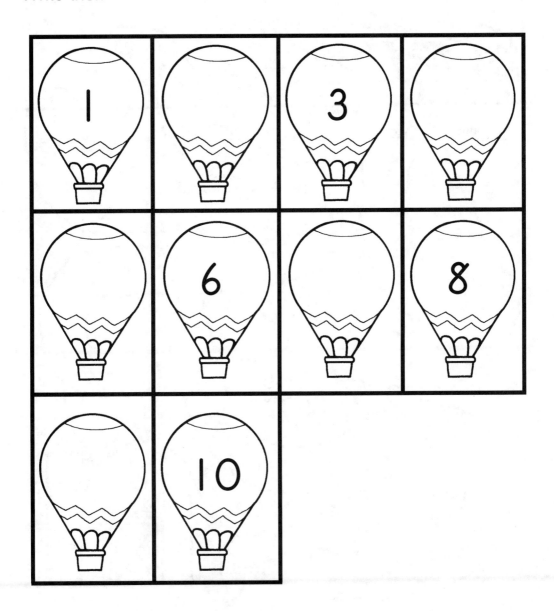

An Amazing Cow

Directions: Complete the maze and help the cow get back to the barn. Follow the numbers in order through the maze.

All Aboard!

Directions: Fill in the missing numbers on the train.

How Many Fish?

Directions: Count the fish in each bowl and circle the correct number.

1 3 2	5 3 4
6 8 7	8 10 9
6 5 4	7 8 9
7 5 6	4 3 2

Birthday Fun

Directions: Draw candles on the cake. Use the number to tell how many to draw.

Cookie Count

Instructions: Draw cookies in the jars. Use the number to tell how many to draw.

38

It's Raining

Directions: Draw raindrops from the clouds. Use the number to tell you how many to draw.

Which Has More?

Directions: Circle the group in each box with a greater number of objects.

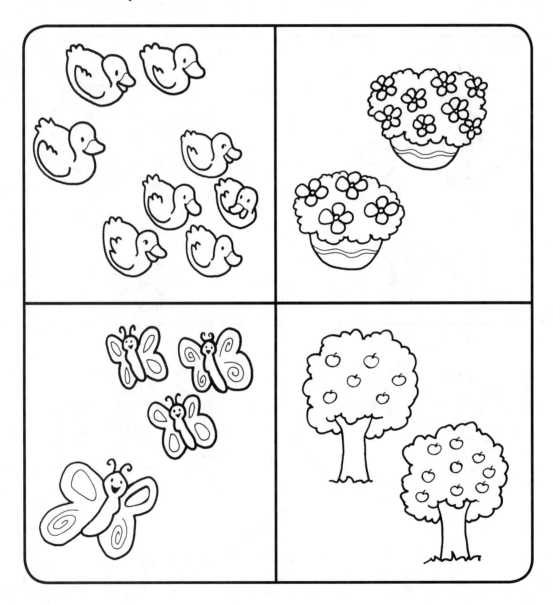

Add the Spots

Directions: Look at the number in each box. Add that number of spots to the animal. Color the animals.

Flower Power

Directions: Color the vase in each row that has the fewest flowers.

42

Special Delivery

Directions: Color the mailbox in each row that has more mail.

Which Is More?

Directions: Write the numerals that show the number of things in each group. Color the group that has more in each row.

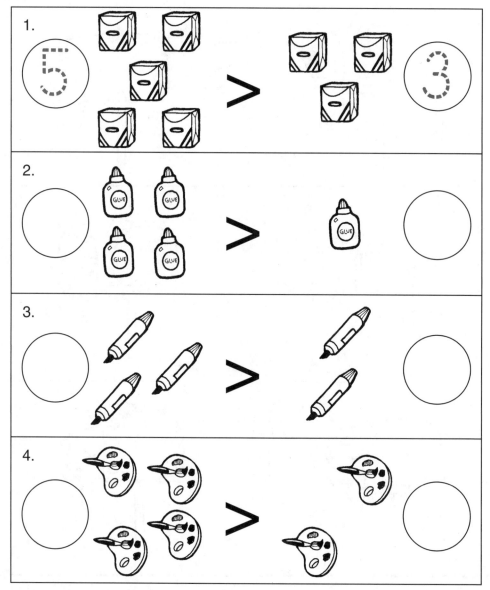

44

Color by Number

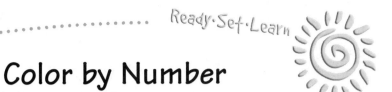

Directions: Color each 8 yellow. Color each 9 red. Color each 10 green.

Party Time

Directions: Draw a line from one set of objects to the set with the same number.

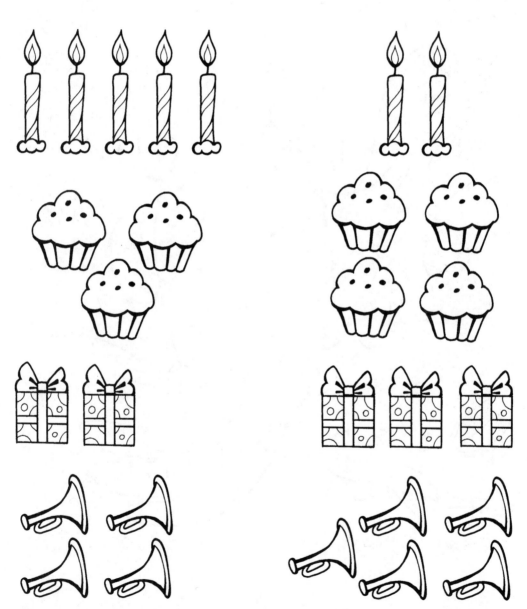

46

Number Match

Directions: Match the groups by drawing a line from each group on the left to the group having the same number on the right.

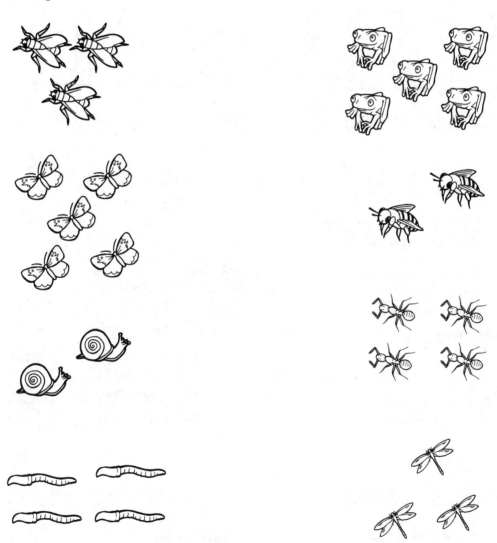

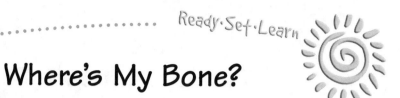

Where's My Bone?

Directions: Find and color the puppy's missing bones. Count the bones and write the number below.

I found 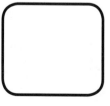 dog bones.

Hide and Seek

Directions: Find and color each fish in the picture. Count the fish and write the number below.

I found ☐ fish in all.

On the Road

Directions: Look at the list of items to find. Count the items and write the number on the line next to the word. Color the picture.

How many can you find?

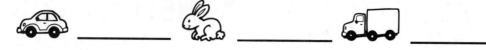

Beach Bears

Directions: Circle the number that tells how many of each thing you can find in the picture.

🏰	1	2	3		⛵	3	4	5
🐻	3	4	5		🔨	2	3	4
🪣	1	2	3		⛱	3	4	5
⚼	1	2	3		☀	1	2	3

This Little Piggy

Directions: Fill in the missing numbers by counting from 1–9.

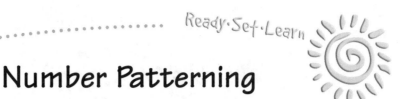

Number Patterning

Directions: Finish the pattern. Use the numbers below to help you.

5 6 5 6 5 6 5 6	
8 7 7 8 7 7 8 7	
6 7 8 6 7 8 6 7	
5 7 6 5 7 6 5 7	

5   6   7   8

What's Missing?

Directions: Fill in the missing numbers in each row.

| 1 | | 3 | 4 |

| 5 | 6 | 7 | |

| 2 | | 4 | 5 |

| 7 | 8 | | 10 |

| 3 | | | 6 |

54

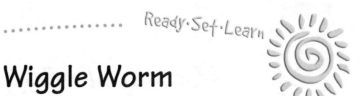

Wiggle Worm

Directions: Fill in the missing numbers in each row.

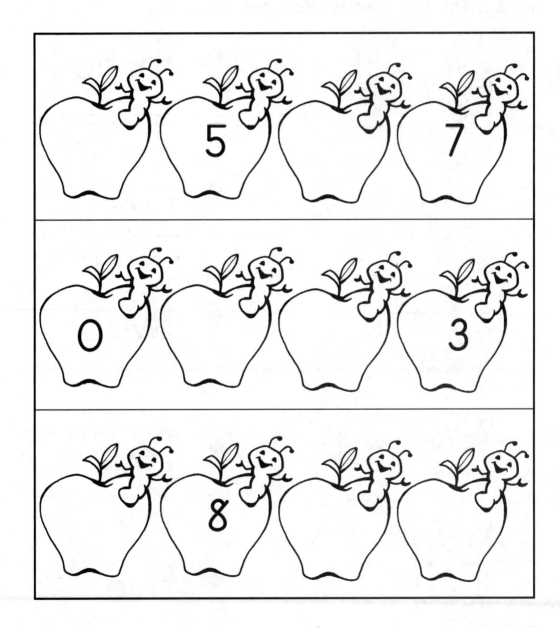

Crown Jewels

Directions: Draw a line from the number set to the number word. (Hint: Count the jewels in each crown.)

• three

• one

• two

• four

• five

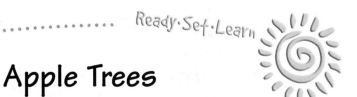

Apple Trees

Directions: Count the apples on each tree. Draw a line from the number word to the tree with the correct number of apples.

seven •

six •

eight •

ten •

nine •

It's in the Bag

Directions: Draw a line to match the number to the word.

zero
three
four
one
five
two

Number Gifts

Directions: Draw a line to match the number to the word.

ten
six
seven
eight
nine

Animal Addition

Directions: Count the animals in each row and add them together. Write the total in the box at the end of the row.

🐱 + 🐱	=
🐶🐶 + 🐶	=
🐦🐦 + 🐦🐦	=
🐹 + 🐹🐹	=
🐢🐢🐢 + 🐢	=

Ball Game!

Directions: Count the objects in each row and add them together. Write the total in the box at the end of the row.

Go Nuts!

Directions: Count the squirrel's nuts in each row and add them together. Write the total in the box at the end of the row.

🌰 + 🌰 🌰 🌰 🌰 =	
🌰 🌰 + 🌰 🌰 🌰 =	
🌰 🌰 🌰 + 🌰 🌰 🌰 =	
🌰 🌰 + 🌰 🌰 =	
🌰 🌰 🌰 + 🌰 🌰 🌰 🌰 =	

This Award
Is Presented To

_____

for

★ Doing Your Best

★ Trying Hard

★ Not Giving Up

★ Making a
Great Effort